One day Kevin and Lotty are
sniffing in the long grass. They
pick up the smell of a fox.

The dogs run after the smell.

They run across the grass very

fast. All of a sudden they stop.

They are at the top of a pit.

They can see Chuff at the bottom
with a fox cub.

The pit is too deep for Chuff

and the cub to get out.

They need help.

Kevin and Lotty see a log on the grass. They push it until one end falls into the pit.

Chuff picks up the fox cub with his teeth. He gets onto the log and he climbs up it.

Chuff drops the fox cub on the grass at the top of the pit. He is glad to be out of the pit.

The cub sees his mum across the grass. He runs off to her. He is glad to be free too.